more
BARNABAS

more
BARNABAS

by
Brother
Graham

URE SMITH • SYDNEY
WOLFE PUBLISHING • LONDON

First published in Australia in 1968
by Ure Smith Pty Ltd,
155 Miller Street, North Sydney, NSW, 2060
and in the United Kingdom in 1968
by Wolfe Publishing Ltd,
10 Earlham Street, London, W.C.2
Copyright © Graham Jeffery, 1968
National Library of Australia Registry No. Aus 68-1622
SBN 72340041 5 (UK edition)
Designed and set in Australia
Printed in Hong Kong
by Peninsula Press Ltd.

'I think I can guess what mine is!'

'Roll on Easter!'

LENT

BUILDING
FUND
£1,000
STILL
NEEDED

'. . . And here in chapel, where one's
thoughts turn invariably to the sacred
mysteries of our religion . . .'

7

'My dear fellow. Do come in and
kneel down!'

'No, Matthew, it's your birthday:
you *snuff out the candles.*'

'. . . And the seat is adjustable for greater leg-room.'

10

'Yes, operator, Perth, please: 𝕻 for
Pharaoh, 𝕰 for Ezekiel, 𝕽 for
Rehoboam, 𝕿 for Thessalonians . . .'

11

'And of course the benefits are not
really apparent until after your death!'

'And which of you girls has been
wearing stiletto heels?'

'Have you anything by the same author?'

ENQUIRIES

'All right then,
boys . . .
Only time for
one prayer each,
remember!'

16

'Of course, I never wear my collar to
these informal gatherings!'

'Quick. Follow that star!'

18

' "Ashes" Wednesday, as you call it,
Brother, has nothing whatever to do
with it!'

'I thought it would be less noticeable
on holiday.'

21

'. . . And stop saying "Nothing like
Lent for the jolly old waistline!" '

'You rang, My Lord?'

'Let us play.'

'Next, the result of the Men's Open
440: Last, Barnabas. One but last,
Cedric. Two but last, Matthew.'

25

'As perhaps some of our younger brethren are aware, this afternoon is the occasion of the Final Test.'

26

'My knees are killing me.'

'Have you seen the Bishop's
umbrella?'

'Have mercy upon us miserable
sinners . . .'

'Moses, my son . . .

Now that you are
old enough . . .

your mother and I felt —

no use pretending
you're still a boy, what!

— *time for you to know, so to speak . . .*

the nature of your . . . um . . . origin . . .

Well, it's like this, Moses, my son (to be quite . . . er . . . blunt with you) . . .

we found you in some bulrushes!'

33

'Somehow it just doesn't seem like Sunday!'

AT REST

....R.I.P....

'And just look at His use of colour
in the left-hand corner!'

38

'. . . And one large frankincense,
please.'

'*And you should have seen the rig-out in the old days!*'

'The usual demands, My Lord:
longer hours, worse conditions; and
an immediate reduction in wages
backdated to Easter '68.'

41

'Of course, you know, I wasn't
always a celibate!'

'What was the first hymn about? I'm
afraid I missed it!'

'I'm very sorry, sir, but all the
uncomfortable chairs are taken.'

'I hope it's not habit-forming!'

47

'And you're sure I can get it on
Higher purchase?'

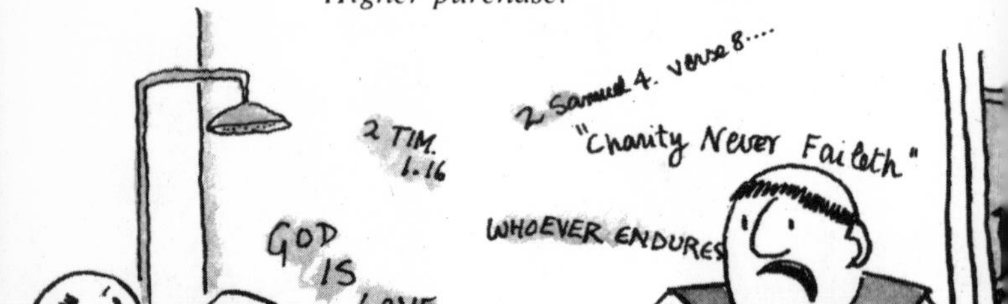

'Who's been writing on the bathroom
walls?'

'Please, Sarah — just one more story
before you go to sleep!'

'Aha! Just in time to join us in a glass
of water!'

'And next, Sister Angela, in a deep velvety black offset with white.'

51

FOR SALE

ONLY ONE
PREVIOUS OWNER

52

'. . . And there's a text in every
packet.'

'Do you always have to bring your
work home with you?'

'About time we got out some fresh posters, Captain.'

'Had any good temptations lately?'

'Three men, sir; and probably in disguise!'

'Well! Moses said it was the
promised land!'

'*A funny thing happened to me on the way to Jericho!*'

59

60 *'I wonder what Moses has brought us this time?'*

'This morning's Epistle is from the
Electricity Board!'

'And precisely which doctor ordered
Brother Anthony on to this special
diet during Lent?'

'We're waiting for the Epilogue!'

'To make matters worse, I'm afraid of heights!'